Name _____

● ● ● ● ● ● ● ● ● ● **BODY SYSTEMS**

RESPIRATORY SYSTEM

The respiratory system brings oxygen into the body and removes carbon dioxide and other gases.

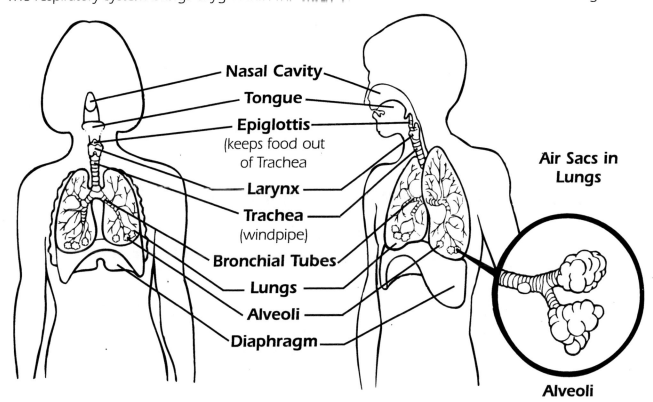

Nasal Cavity

Tongue

Epiglottis
(keeps food out
of Trachea)

Larynx

Trachea
(windpipe)

Bronchial Tubes

Lungs

Alveoli

Diaphragm

Air Sacs in
Lungs

Alveoli

BREATHING

When you breathe in, the diaphragm contracts (becomes smaller) and drops down. The ribs expand outward. Air rushes in to fill the space.

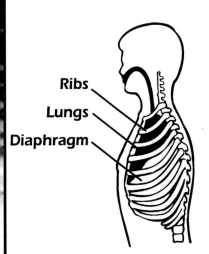

Ribs

Lungs

Diaphragm

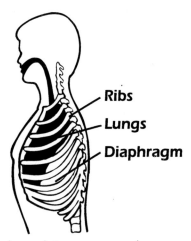

Ribs

Lungs

Diaphragm

When you breathe out, the diaphragm relaxes into an upward position. The ribs settle downward. The space now shrinks and air is forced out of the lungs.

The air you inhale is warmed in the passages, filtered by the coarse hairs and mucus inside the nose, and moistened by mucus in the nasal passages, throat, and trachea (windpipe) before it reaches your lungs.

1

Name _____   Date _____

OXYGEN INTAKE

Your blood contains about one quart of oxygen. When you are very active you breathe faster to take in extra oxygen needed for the increased activity. You can measure how fast your cells are working by measuring how fast your cells use oxygen. Test your rate at various times during the day and after different activities. Your oxygen intake is measured by the number of breaths you take per minute.

Compare your chart with others.

OXYGEN INTAKE		
ACTIVITY	**RATE** (breaths per minute)	**TIME**
1.		
2.		
3.		
4.		
5.		
6.		
7.		
8.		
9.		
10.		
11.		
12.		

MP3408 Body Systems

Name _____ Date _____

RESPIRATION

1. Explain the main function of the respiratory system ___ _____

   _____

   _____

2. Explain why you breathe faster during increased activity. _____

   _____

   _____

3. Cold air is _____ in the passages, _____ by the hairs and mucus in the linings, and _____ by the mucus on its way to the lungs.

4. You breathe _____ in and breathe out _____.

Fill in the blanks with the following information:

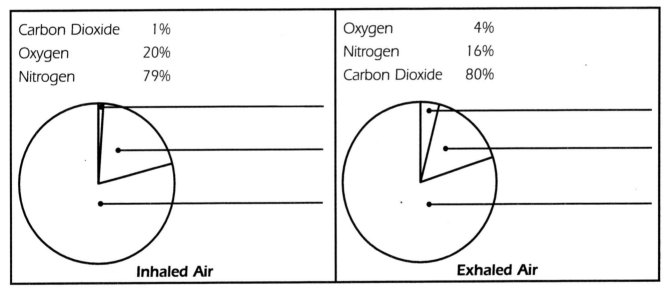

Carbon Dioxide	1%
Oxygen	20%
Nitrogen	79%

Inhaled Air

Oxygen	4%
Nitrogen	16%
Carbon Dioxide	80%

Exhaled Air

Complete three activities.

1. Explain what causes yawning.
2. Report on what hay fever is and what can be done for those who suffer from this condition.
3. Go to a store and make a list of several of the remedies available for the common cold. Tell what each one claims it can do to relieve the symptoms.
4. Describe what a cold is and what causes coughs.
5. Explain what causes hiccups.
6. Draw a side-view diagram of the inside of your mouth and nasal cavity. Include and label the soft and hard palate, tongue, tonsils, trachea, esophagus, adenoids, epiglottis, and mandible.

Name _____ Date _____

DIGESTIVE SYSTEM

The main function of the digestive system is to change food, through chemical action, into substances the body can use.

Tongue
Moves food around

Esophagus
Passageway for food between mouth and stomach.

Liver
Produces digestive juice called bile,

Gall Bladder
Stores bile until needed for digestion.

Duodenum
First 10–12 inches of the small intestine.

Appendix
An organ that no longer has a function in your body.

Rectum
Lowest part of large intestine–solid waste held until released from the body.

Salivary Glands
Secrete juices into the mouth.

Stomach
Stores food while enzymes break down food for further digestion.

Pancreas
Produces pancreatic juices to further break down food in digestion.

Small Intestine
Nutrients for the body are absorbed and moved into blood stream. Here the process of digestion is completed.

Large Intestine
Absorbs water, leaving more solid material which body cannot use. Indigestible material is stored for approximately 24 to 30 hours before leaving body.

Anus
Skin opening that expels waste from body.

Enlarged picture of inside of small intestine showing the villi that line the walls.

4

Name _____   Date _____

DIGESTIVE SYSTEM

Use the illustration on page 4. Fill in the blanks as you follow the process of digestion.

1. Food is the body's fuel. The materials the body needs to run properly come from the food and drink we consume. The process of changing food to substances the body can use is called _____.

2. Digestion begins in the _____. The instant food enters the mouth, the _____ _____ send secretions in to begin changing starches into usable sugar.

3. The _____ moves food around. Teeth further break up food into small pieces and reduce it to a small, soft ball ready for swallowing.

4. Food moves down the _____ toward the _____ by muscular movements called peristalsis. When it reaches the stomach, some of the food is stored temporarily, and further digestion takes place. Chemicals called enzymes are produced by the stomach. They also act to break down the food. Powerful stomach muscles grind and churn the food while strong digestive juices, called gastric juices, make proteins digestible. The food is broken down into a thick, pasty juice called chyme. The process takes three to four hours.

5. At this point, some of this digested "food" is absorbed into the _____ _____.

6. The rest is slowly released into the _____ _____ through a "door" at the end of the stomach called the pylorus. This "door" is necessary to keep the food in the stomach long enough to be digested.

7. As the semi-digested food passes into the next 10 or 12 inches of the small intestine, called the _____, it is further acted upon by digestive juices.

8. Bile from the _____ is stored in the _____ _____.

9. Bile is released to break down fats. The _____ produces pancreatic juices and sends them into this section to carry on further digestion. Tiny, fingerlike projections called villi line the inside of the small intestine. The villi absorb the nourishing chemicals from the food. Blood vessels carry these chemicals to all parts of the body.

10. Water is absorbed in the _____ _____, leaving the more solid material which cannot be used. This waste has not been digested.

11. It will finally be released from the body through the _____ and expelled out an opening in the skin called the _____.

chyme (kīm)
duodenum (dyü ə'dē nəm)
peristalsis (per ə 'stol səs)
pylorus (pī'lōr'əs)

Name _____   Date _____

DIGESTIVE SYSTEM

Arrange the following in the proper order to show the correct path food takes through the digestive system. It takes from 10 to 24 hours to complete the cycle of digestion.

esophagus	small intestine	rectum	tongue	duodenum
stomach	large intestine	mouth	anus	

1. _____   4. _____   7. _____

2. _____   5. _____   8. _____

3. _____   6. _____   9. _____

Taste Areas of the Tongue

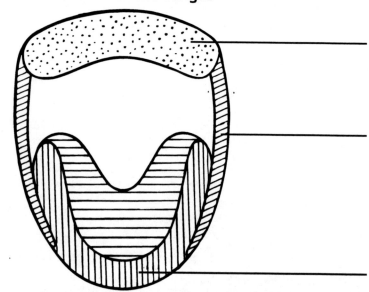

The tongue performs four main functions:

A. helps chew food

B. helps swallow food

C. Its surface is covered with taste buds to experience various tastes.

Edges-sour and acid

Front-salt and sweet

Back-bitter

D. helps to form sounds by moving freely up and down as we speak.

10. Using the information above, label the tastes that each section of the tongue senses.

11. Why can we sometimes hear noises in the stomach during digestion? _____

_____

_____

12. Explain why food stays so long in the stomach before being allowed to pass gradually into the small intestine. _____

_____

_____

13. Report on one of the following disorders of the digestive tract:

    gallstones   constipation   colitis   heartburn   ulcers

6

EXCRETORY SYSTEM

The main function of the excretory system is to remove waste from the body.

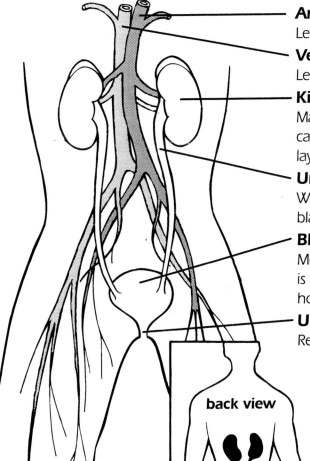

Artery
Leads away from the heart.

Vein
Leads to the heart.

Kidneys (2)
Main organs of excretory system. Act as filters to capture waste. They are protected by lower ribs and layers of fat.

Ureters
Waste drains from kidneys through ureters into bladder.

Bladder
Muscular bag in lower abdomen Waste from kidneys is stored until released from body. Adult bladder can hold about one quart (0.946 1) of fluid.

Urethra
Releases waste in the form of urine from the body.

back view

> 200 liters of blood are filtered daily by the kidneys. The usable material is sent into the blood stream. Waste is drained into the bladder.

Other Organs Involved in Removing Waste from the Body

Liver

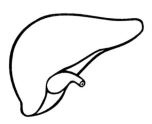

cleans waste particles from blood

Lungs

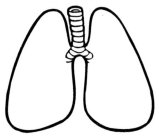

remove carbon dioxide and water from blood

Skin

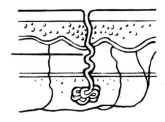

gives off perspiration (water and dissolved mineral salts)

BODY SYSTEMS

EXCRETORY SYSTEM

Fill in the blanks below with the correct words from the list.

ureters	bladder	urethra	ribs
artery	vein	blood	heart

1. Your kidneys are protected by _____ and fat.

2. A muscular bag that stores urine before it is eliminated from the body is the _____.

3. The _____ are tubes leading from your kidneys to your bladder through which waste fluid drains.

4. Urine exits the body through the _____.

5. Blood enters the excretory system through a/an _____.

Match the organ with its function. Put the letter of the organ on the line to indicate your choice of answers.

6. _____ Filter liquid waste from the blood   A. sweat glands in skin

7. _____ Filters solid particles in the blood   B. lungs

8. _____ Undigested solid foods are stored and removed   C. liver

9. _____ Gives off perspiration   D. kidneys

10. _____ Help protect the kidneys from injury   E. urethra

11. _____ Pumps blood throughout the body   F. large intestine and rectum

12. _____ Remove carbon dioxide and water from blood   G. lower ribs

13. _____ Liquid waste passes out of the body through this organ   H. heart

Complete the following activities:

14. Find out why urine is yellow.

15. Find out about a kidney transplant and make a report telling what it is and why it could be necessary.

16. What causes diarrhea?

17. What causes constipation?

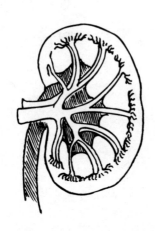

MP3408 Body Systems

BODY SYSTEMS

CIRCULATORY SYSTEM AND BLOOD

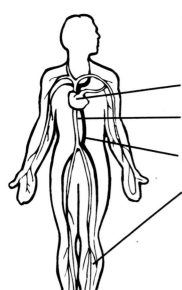

The circulatory system is a group of organs which carry food and oxygen to and remove waste from every cell in the body.

Heart—Pump of the system

Veins—Lead **to** the heart

Arteries—Lead **away from** the heart

Capillaries—Smallest blood vessels

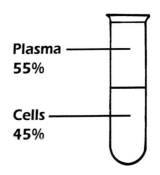

Plasma 55%

Cells 45%

Composition of blood

THE BLOOD—FLUID OF THE CIRCULATORY SYSTEM

Red Blood Cells

- Carry oxygen and carbon dioxide to and from the lungs
- Produced in the bone marrow
- Living cells without a nucleus
- About 5,000,000 per cubic millimeter
- Live only about 100–120 days

White Blood Cells

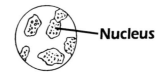

Nucleus

- Destroy bacteria which invade the body
- Are produced in the spleen and lymph nodes
- Are living cells with nuclei
- About 6,000 per cubic millimeter

Blood Platelets

- Aid blood clotting
- Are formed from bone cells in bone marrow
- Are nonliving cells
- Help stop bleeding by forming clots
- About 300,000 per cubic millimeter

Plasma

- Liquid part of blood
- About 90% water
- Contains salts and chemicals
- Moves through veins and arteries

Composition of Blood

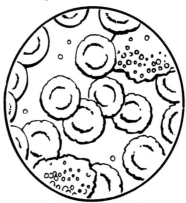

Human Blood Magnified

MP3408 Body Systems

Name _____   Date _____

CIRCULATORY SYSTEM

W O R D   S E A R C H

```
A  H  B  B  C  D  E  V  F  S  H  J  S  X  C
C  E  D  L  E  Y  F  E  Z  A  L  B  L  S  W
M  A  R  R  O  W  H  I  T  A  S  K  L  A  D
A  R  Q  B  Y  O  G  N  G  M  E  C  E  L  L
O  T  Z  M  X  N  D  S  M  S  I  N  C  T  Q
S  X  L  Y  K  R  M  U  I  A  R  T  D  S  E
P  K  G  W  V  J  I  U  L  L  E  P  E  V  J
R  E  N  U  C  L  E  U  S  P  T  O  R  P  R
N  P  L  A  T  E  L  E  T  S  R  N  O  S  F
Q  C  H  E  M  I  C  A  L  S  A  T  G  I  H
```

OXYGEN   VEINS
BLOOD   RED CELLS
PLATELETS   CHEMICALS
CELL   ARTERIES
HEART   MARROW
PLASMA   SALTS
NUCLEUS

Complete the sentences below by adding the correct vowels.

1. R ___ d bl ___ ___ d c ___ lls c ___ rr ___ ___ x ___ g ___ n ___ nd
   c ___ rb ___ n d ___ ___ x ___ d ___ .

2. Wh ___ t ___ bl ___ ___ d c ___ lls d ___ str ___ ___ b ___ ct ___ r ___ ___ .

3. Bl ___ ___ d pl ___ t ___ l ___ ts ___ ___ d bl ___ ___ d cl ___ tt ___ ng.

4. Th ___ h ___ ___ rt ___ s th ___ p ___ mp ___ f th ___ c ___ rc ___ l ___ t ___ r ___
   s ___ st ___ m.

5. Th ___ fl ___ ___ d ___ f th ___ c ___ rc ___ l ___ t ___ r ___ s ___ st ___ m
   ___ s bl ___ ___ d.

Complete the sentences below by adding the correct consonants.

6. ___ a ___ i ___ ___ a ___ ie ___ a ___ e ___ ___ e ___ ___ a ___ ___ e ___ ___
   ___ ___ oo ___ ___ e ___ ___ e ___ ___ .

7. A ___ ___ e ___ ie ___ ___ e a ___ a ___ ay ___ ___ o ___ ___ ___ e ___ ea ___ ___ .

8. ___ ei ___ ___ ___ ea ___ ___ o ___ ___ e ___ ea ___ ___ .

9. ___ ___ e ___ i ___ ___ u ___ a ___ o ___ y ___ y ___ ___ e ___ ___ ___ i ___ ___ ___
   ___ oo ___ a ___ ___ o ___ y ___ e ___ ___ o ___ e ___ .

10. ___ ___ a ___ ___ a i ___ ___ ___ e ___ i ___ ui ___ ___ a ___ ___ ___ o
    ___ ___ oo ___ .

MP3408 Body Systems

Name _____   Date _____

THE HEART

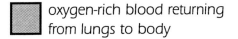

deoxygenated blood coming
from body to lungs

oxygen-rich blood returning
from lungs to body

Head and Arms

Superior Vena Cava

Aorta
To all parts of the body

Right Lung

Pulmonary Artery

Left Lung

Pulmonary Vein

Left Atrium

Right Atrium

Left Ventricle

Right Ventricle

Septum

Lower Part of Body

Inferior Vena Cava

MP3408 Body Systems

THE PATH OF BLOOD

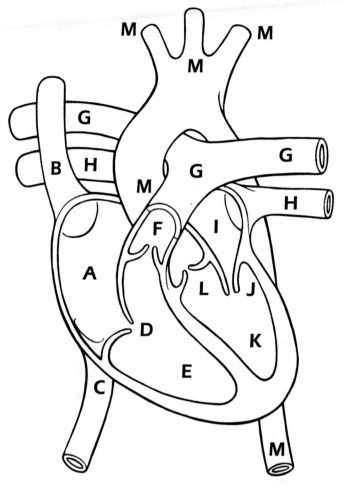

The **RIGHT ATRIUM (A)**, which is the upper chamber of the right side of the heart, receives blood from the upper body through the **SUPERIOR VENA CAVA (B)**, and from the lower body through the **INFERIOR VENA CAVA (C)**. This blood is a darker color because it is returning from the body carrying carbon dioxide (waste from cells) that was released by body cells as the blood deposited oxygen. Blood then flows through the **TRICUSPID VALVE (D)** into the **RIGHT VENTRICLE (E)** which is the lower chamber on the right side of the heart. Through contraction of the right ventricle, the darker-colored blood is forced through the **PULMONARY VALVE (F)** into the **PULMONARY ARTERY (G)**. The **PULMONARY ARTERY (G)** branches to both the right and the

left lung to pick up oxygen and release carbon dioxide wastes. While in the lungs, the blood changes color to a bright red because it is now full of fresh oxygen needed by the body. It returns from both lungs through the **PULMONARY VEINS (H)**.

The red blood carrying oxygen for all body cells will now re-enter the left upper chamber of the heart, the **LEFT ATRIUM (I)**. It then flows through the **MITRAL VALVE (J)** and into the lower left chamber, the **LEFT VENTRICLE (K)**. Finally, the oxygenated blood passes through the **AORTIC VALVE (L)** into the **AORTA (M)**, the largest artery, where it is sent to all parts of the body.

MP3408 Body Systems

Name _____   Date _____

THE HEART

Use the information on page 12 to complete these activities:

1. Label these parts of the heart:

right atrium	pulmonary artery	valves—tricuspid
left atrium	pulmonary vein	pulmonary
right ventricle	superior vena cava	mitral
left ventricle	inferior vena cava	aortic

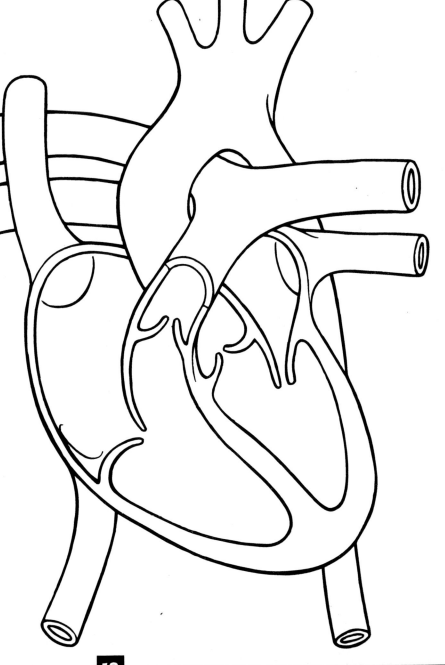

2. Lightly shade the sections blue that transport blood carrying carbon dioxide to the lungs.

3. Lightly shade the sections red that carry blood with a fresh supply of oxygen from the lungs to the body.

4. Draw arrows on the heart diagram to show the path blood takes on its journey through the heart.

MP3408 Body Systems

Name _____   Date _____

REVIEW

1. Explain the function of the heart in the circulatory system. _____

   _____

   _____

2. _____ carry blood to the heart.

3. _____ carry blood away from the heart.

4. The largest artery in the body that goes from the heart is called the _____.

5. Arrange the following words to show the correct flow of blood through the heart: superior vena cava, right ventricle, left ventricle, right atrium, left atrium, pulmonary vein, pulmonary artery, aorta.

   A. _____   E. _____

   B. _____   F. _____

   C. _____   G. _____

   D. _____   H. _____

6. Blood contains _____ that carry oxygen to the cells and wastes away from the cells.

7. The _____ fight bacteria that enter the body.

8. Blood contains _____ that are necessary for blood clotting.

9. _____ is the liquid part of the blood.

10. Describe the function of the lungs in the circulatory system. _____

    _____

    _____

11. Blood going to the heart is _____ in color, while blood going away from the heart is _____ in color.

12. Why do you think it would be very dangerous to lose a quart of blood in an accident?

    _____

    _____

    _____

    _____

    _____

    _____

14

Name _____ Date _____

NERVOUS SYSTEM

The nervous system helps you respond to the world around you.
This system has two main divisions:

Nervous System
(Brain, Spinal Cord, Nerves)

Central Nervous System	Peripheral Nervous System

- Brain
- Spinal Cord
- It controls behavior.

- Nerves
- It serves internal organs.
- It is a pathway to the brain for the five senses.
- It helps you respond to the world around you.

The brain is divided into three main parts.

Cerebrum —
Controls higher processes and senses (speech, reasoning, memory, motor, smell, touch, taste, sight, hearing)

Cerebellum —
Coordinates motor movement

Medulla —
Controls involuntary reflexes

Scalp —
Skull —
(protects brain)
Spinal Nerve —
Spinal Cord —
Spinal Column —
(protects spinal cord)

Left Hemisphere   **Right Hemisphere**

Cerebrum

Cerebellum

Back View of Brain

Brain cells, once destroyed by injury, disease, or birth defects, cannot grow back. Their damage is irreversible.

15

NERVOUS SYSTEM

The individual nerve cell, or neuron, is the basic unit that carries out the work of the nervous system.

Nerve cells have "feelers" attached. These feelers can be compared to electrical wires. Impulses or messages can jump across these feelers from one cell to another. This jumping across the feelers is called a **synapse**.

Impulses going to a nerve cell travel along the feelers called **dendrites** (or receivers).

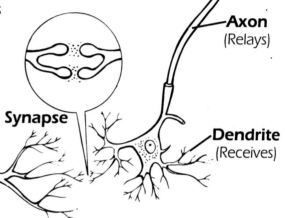

Neuron—A Nerve Cell

Axon (Relays)

Synapse

Dendrite (Receives)

Nucleus

Axon (Relays)

Dendrite (Receives)

Impulse

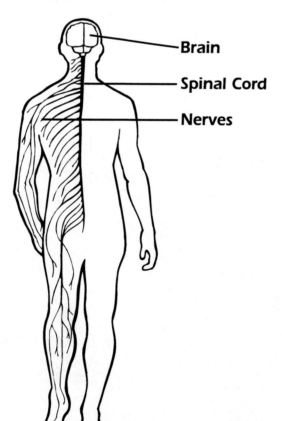

Brain

Spinal Cord

Nerves

Impulses leaving a nerve cell travel along the feelers called **axons** (or senders).

All impulses must go through at least one of the body's switchboards—either the brain or the spinal cord. From the switchboard, impulses are sent along the axons and through the dendrites to the nerve cells of the organ that must react to the stimulus. This might be a muscle or a gland.

A response which is involuntary such as breathing, digesting food, or pulling away from something hot is called a **reflex action**. Voluntary actions are those we perform with our conscious mind such as reading, speaking, or walking.

MP3408 Body Systems

Name _____   Date _____

NERVOUS SYSTEM

Some messages that the sensory nerves (located all over our body) send are marked **urgent**. They are usually messages of pain. An immediate action is necessary to relieve some discomfort. All these reactions are called **reflexes**. A reflex is an automatic reaction to some sense message, like pain. The information gets processed in your spinal cord. Your muscles begin to react immediately even before your brain gets the news of what is happening. This bypass is called a **reflex arc**.

Spinal Cord

Receptor Sensory cells in skin receive stimulus

Reflex Center

Reflex Action

Reflex Arc

Effector Muscle or gland react to stimulus

Explain how each of the following reflexes serve a useful purpose.

1. The blinking of an eye _____

_____

2. Pulling finger back from heat _____

3. Increased heartbeat during exercise _____

_____

4. Elimination of waste from the body _____

_____

5. Taste, sight, or smell of food stimulates the flow of saliva in mouth.

_____

_____

6. Spitting out a bad-tasting food _____

_____

7. A fever _____

_____

Name _____   Date _____

BODY SYSTEMS

REVIEW

1. Name the main parts of the nervous system.

   A. _____   B. _____   C. _____

2. What function does the brain perform in our nervous system? _____

   _____

   _____

3. The brain and spinal cord are very delicate organs. Each is housed in areas which give them special protection. The brain is protected by the _____, and the spinal cord is protected by the _____ _____.

4. Some responses to our environment are controlled by our brain and are called voluntary. Other responses are involuntary and are performed without our brain becoming involved in the decision. Write V on the blanks for voluntary responses and I for involuntary responses.

   A. _____ breathing   F. _____ singing

   B. _____ talking   G. _____ reading

   C. _____ swimming   H. _____ heart beating

   D. _____ blood circulation   I. _____ pronouncing a recognized word

   E. _____ pulling finger out of a fire   J. _____ digesting food

5. Why does brain damage due to injuries, diseases, or birth defects have such a serious consequence on our lives? _____

   _____

   _____

6. A nerve cell is called a _____.

7. The _____ is the largest part of your brain and makes up about 85% of the brain's weight. It regulates posture, balance, and movement and controls actions guided by your own will.

8. The _____ coordinates movements and helps muscles work together.

9. The _____ regulates the involuntary action of the lungs, heartbeat, digestion, and secretions of glands.

10. Some _____ actions are an automatic response to a stimulus.

MP3408 Body Systems

SKELETAL SYSTEM

The skeletal system supports the structure of the body, gives it shape, protects vital organs, and serves as an attachment for the muscles.

Bones are alive. They take in food (calcium, phosphates) through blood. They grow. They repair themselves.

Bones can be divided into living tissue, cells, blood vessels, mineral deposits, and water.

45% Mineral Deposits

25% Water

30% Living Tissue, Cells, Blood Vessels

Periosteum

Spongy Bone
Porous, contains blood vessels, lymph vessels, nerves

Marrow

Compact Bone
Hard, outer surface of bone

Periosteum—Soft, thin substance that covers and protects the bone.

Compact Bone—Tough, hard bone that can heal itself when broken.

Spongy Bone—Contains red marrow which produces red blood cells that carry oxygen and carbon dioxide throughout the body.

Marrow—Soft, inner center of bones containing blood vessels and fat cells. Manufactures red blood cells.

Kinds of Joints

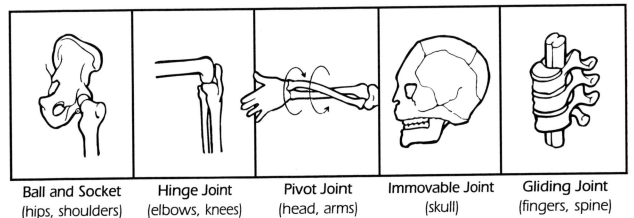

| Ball and Socket (hips, shoulders) | Hinge Joint (elbows, knees) | Pivot Joint (head, arms) | Immovable Joint (skull) | Gliding Joint (fingers, spine) |

Name _____   Date _____

SKELETAL SYSTEM

The human skeleton contains 206 bones.

1. List the main functions of the skeleton.

   A. _____

   B. _____

   C. _____

   D. _____

2. The bones of the skeleton are held together at the joints by ligaments and tendons. Bones are covered with a special tissue called

   _____.

The skeletal system is divided into two parts:

1. **Axial Skeleton**
   skull (protects brain)
   ribs (protect lungs, heart)
   spinal column (houses and protects spinal cord)

2. **Appendicular Skeleton**
   legs
   pelvis
   arms
   shoulders

Our joints are covered with a thick pad of smooth cartilage which acts as a buffer between the hard bones.

There are four main shapes of bones in the skeleton:
   flat—ribs, shoulder blades
   irregular—vertebrae, tiny ear bones
   short—wrist, ankle
   long—arms, legs, fingers

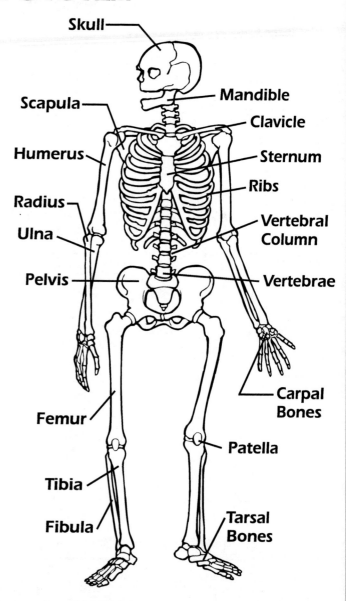

Skull — Mandible — Scapula — Clavicle — Humerus — Sternum — Radius — Ribs — Ulna — Vertebral Column — Pelvis — Vertebrae — Femur — Carpal Bones — Patella — Tibia — Fibula — Tarsal Bones

3. Draw a circle around four ball and socket joints.
4. Draw an **X** on four hinge joints.
5. Draw a star ★ on two gliding joints.
6. Draw two arrows ➡ showing where a pivot joint is located.
7. Draw an arrow ➡ showing where the immovable joints are located.

MP3408 Body Systems

Name _____   Date _____

SKELETAL SYSTEM

Use the information on pages 19 and 20 to complete these sentences.

1. The collarbone is called the _____.

2. The patella is better known as your _____.

3. The _____ and _____ make up the lower leg.

4. The _____ and _____ make up the lower arm.

5. Ball and socket joints can be found in the _____ and _____.

6. The _____ has bones in it that have fused together and are immovable.

7. Your breastbone is also known as your _____.

8. The hipbone is known as the _____.

9. The thighbone is a long bone called the _____.

10. The skull is composed of 22 bones. All but one are immovable. Name the one bone that can move in your skull. _____

11. Explain why "hinge" is an appropriate name for the joints at your knees and elbows.

    _____

    _____

12. Name the four main functions of the skeleton.

    A. _____

    B. _____

    C. _____

    D. _____

13. The skeleton is made up of _____ bones.

14. Name the two parts of the skeletal system.

    A. _____   B. _____

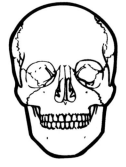 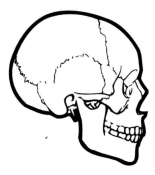

MP3408 Body Systems

Name _____   Date _____

BODY SYSTEMS

REVIEW

Write the letter of the correct answer on the blank in front of each word.

1. _____ Marrow

2. _____ Skeleton

3. _____ Calcium

4. _____ Periosteum

5. _____ Ligament

6. _____ Cartilage

7. _____ Axial skeleton

8. _____ Appendicular skeleton

9. _____ Vertebrae

10. _____ Spinal cord

A. smooth tissue that acts as a buffer between bones

B. large bunch of nerves that pass through your spine

C. part of your skeleton that includes skull, ribs, and spinal cord

D. substance in the center of the bones

E. the outer covering of bones

F. the irregular bones that make up the spinal column

G. tissue that fastens your bones together

H. the part of your skeleton made up of your arms, legs, pelvis, and shoulders

I. framework of your body

J. the mineral found in bones

Answer the following questions.

11. Why are joints necessary? _____

_____

12. Why is your backbone so important to you? _____

_____

_____

13. How does your skeleton compare to the steel framework of a skyscraper?

_____

_____

14. Why do bones of older people break more easily than those of a younger person?

_____

_____

15. Explain why a proper diet is important to your bones. _____

_____

_____

22

Name _____ Date _____

MUSCULAR SYSTEM

Some Important Skeletal Muscles
Muscles help control the movement of your body.

Pectoral
Lowers the arm

Intercostals
Between ribs help you catch your breath and turn the upper half of your body

Quadriceps
Help straighten your knees— useful in climbing stairs

Biceps Femoris
Extends thigh or bends knee

Muscles surround your bones and body organs. They give form and support, make movement possible, and produce heat.

Sternocleidomastoid
Rotates the heavy head

Deltoid
Shoulder muscles
Raise the upper arm

Triceps Help raise and
Biceps lower arms

Gluteus Maximus
Strong muscles— Straightens the hip joint and holds you upright

Gastrocnemius
Helps you stand on your toes

Tendons
Connective tissue

Three Kinds of Muscles

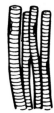

Skeletal—Voluntary
Move skeleton

Example:
triceps   gastrocnemius
biceps   tongue
quadriceps   pectorals

Smooth—Involuntary
Move internal organs

Example:
diaphragm   stomach
esophagus   blood vessels

Cardiac—Automatic

heart

23

BODY SYSTEMS

THREE KINDS OF MUSCLES

Write A, B, or C on the blanks to show the correct muscle type.

A. Smooth	**B. Skeletal**	**C. Cardiac**
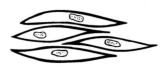		

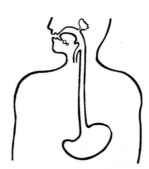

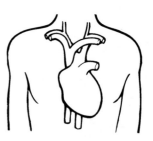

1. Bicep _____

2. Tricep _____

4. Tongue _____

5. Esophagus _____

6. Stomach _____

8. Heart _____

9. Blood Vessels _____

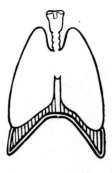

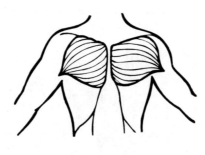

3. Diaphragm _____

7. Pectorals _____

10. Quadriceps _____

11. Gastrocnemius _____

12. Sternocleidomastoid (neck muscles) _____

24

Name _____   Date _____

MUSCLE PUZZLE

ACROSS

2. Muscles surround your _____ and body organs.
3. This type of muscle tissue moves internal organs.
4. Muscles, when moving, produce body _____.
5. Connective tissue of muscles
7. You control the movement of these muscles.
8. _____ muscle tissue moves the heart.
9. The heart muscle _____ between each beat.

DOWN

1. Muscles that move and work without our control
3. This muscle tissue moves the skeleton.
4. Cardiac muscle controls the _____.
6. Biceps, triceps, and deltoids are all _____.

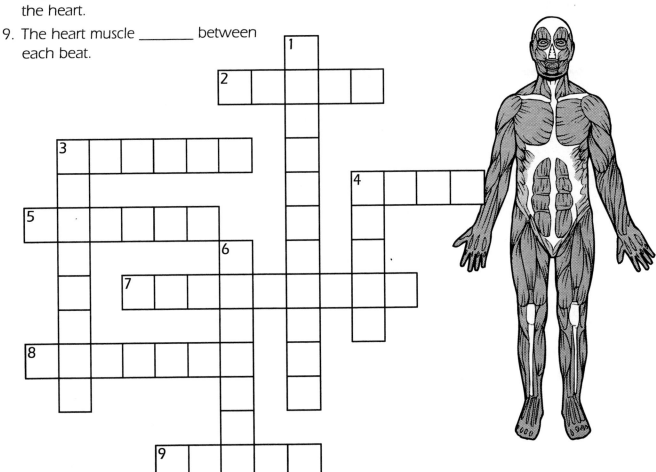

Use reference sources to find out and explain why you shiver when you are cold.

_____

_____

Name _____   Date _____

REVIEW

Name the main parts of each body system. Briefly explain the main function of each system.

1. **Respiratory** _____

_____

_____

2. **Digestive** _____

_____

_____

3. **Excretory** _____

_____

_____

4. **Circulatory** _____

_____

_____

5. **Nervous** _____

_____

_____

_____

6. **Skeletal** _____

_____

_____

_____

_____

7. **Muscular** _____

_____

_____

_____

_____

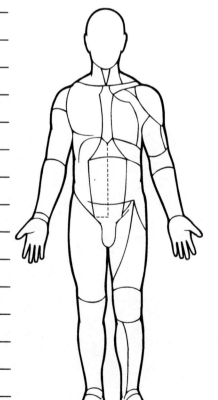

MP3408 Body Systems

BODY SYSTEMS

REVIEW

On line **A**, write the name of the body part pictured.

On line **B**, write the name of the body system in which the part functions.

	Nervous	Digestive	Excretory
Circulatory	Respiratory	Muscular	Skeletal

A. _____	A. _____	A. _____	A. _____
B. _____	B. _____	B. _____	B. _____

A. _____	A. _____	A. _____	A. _____
B. _____	B. _____	B. _____	B. _____

A. _____	A. _____	A. _____	A. _____
B. _____	B. _____	B. _____	B. _____

A. _____	A. _____	A. _____	A. _____
B. _____	B. _____	B. _____	B. _____

A. _____	A. _____	A. _____	A. _____
B. _____	B. _____	B. _____	B. _____

Name _____   Date _____

BODY SYSTEMS

REVIEW

Write the letters of the answers on the blanks.

_____	1. Consists of 206 bones	**A.** carbon dioxide
_____	2. Neuron	**B.** alveoli
_____	3. Main organs of the excretory system	**C.** lungs
_____	4. Color of blood in the veins	**D.** muscles
_____	5. Color of blood in the arteries	**E.** liver
_____	6. The muscular tube that moves food to the stomach	**F.** skull
_____	7. Soft-walled upper chambers of the heart	**G.** skeleton
_____	8. Largest artery of the body	**H.** cardiac
_____	9. Air sacs in clusters in the lungs	**I.** bluish
_____	10. Manufactures blood cells in the bones	**J.** oxygen
_____	11. Small finger-like projections in the small intestines	**K.** esophagus
_____	12. Digestion is completed here	**L.** cerebrum
_____	13. Largest part of the brain	**M.** nerve cell
_____	14. Bundle of nerves leading to the brain	**N.** smooth
_____	15. Waste gas given off by the body	**O.** aorta
_____	16. Gas needed to maintain life	**P.** villi
_____	17. Protects organs of the upper body	**Q.** bright red
_____	18. Filters out solid waste particles of the blood	**R.** epiglottis
_____	19. Gives form and support to the body making movement possible	**S.** atriums
_____	20. Involuntary muscles	**T.** spinal cord
_____	21. Voluntary muscles	**U.** skeletal
_____	22. Part of the skeleton with immovable joints	**V.** kidneys
_____	23. Flap of skin that keeps food out of the trachea	**W.** small intestines
_____	24. Muscles of the heart	**X.** ribs
_____	25. Removes carbon dioxide and water from blood.	**Y.** marrow

28

BODY SYSTEMS BACKGROUND MATERIAL

Pages 1–3: The respiratory system brings oxygen into the body and removes carbon dioxide and other gases.

The air one inhales passes through the pharynx at the back of the throat and through the larynx, or voice box. The larynx is sometimes called the Adam's Apple. From there, air moves down the trachea. There is a flap of skin, the epiglottis, at the top of the trachea that snaps shut to prevent food from entering and causing choking. The cleaned air then passes into two bronchial tubes. One goes to the right lung and one to the left lung. The bronchial tubes take air directly into and out of the lungs. Each bronchi divides into many smaller tubes which narrow more and more until they end in the alveoli—the tiny air sacs that fill the lungs. There are about 600 million of these tiny sacs. This is where oxygen from the air passes into the blood and carbon dioxide passes out of the blood into the air sacs. This waste gas is passed out of the body when one exhales.

Inside the trunk is the chest cavity. Most of this area is filled with lungs that are actually the size of a pair of footballs. The floor of this 'room' is called the diaphragm.

Pages 4–6: The materials the body needs to keep running properly are extracted through complicated processes from consumed food and drink. These chemicals are then sent throughout the body to help repair, rebuild, and replace that which the body has burned, used, or discarded.

Digestion begins in the mouth. The instant food enters the mouth, the salivary glands send in secretions to begin breaking down starches into usable sugar. This is a reflex action. Saliva can begin flowing even with the sight or smell of food!

Lining the inside of the small intestine are finger-like projections called villi. The villi absorb the nourishing chemicals. Blood vessels carry these chemicals to all parts of the body. The small intestine is about 20 feet long, while the large intestine is about 5 feet long. The entire digestive system is a flexible, mucus-lined muscular tube about 24 to 36 feet long.

Pages 7–8: The excretory system, along with other systems' organs, helps to remove body waste safely. The kidneys—main organs of this system—are filters. There are two of them located near the spine in the middle of the back. They are protected by lower ribs and covered by layers of fat. This protection is necessary, for if anything happened to these important filters, it would not take long before the body's system would be poisoned by its own waste. It is possible, however, to function with only one kidney.

Waste drains out of the kidneys in the form of urine. Urine is about 95% water and 5% urea (protein from protein breakdown). Fresh urine has no bacteria in it. It is quite clean; in fact, probably cleaner than one's own hands or the sandwich eaten for lunch.

Pages 9–14: The circulatory system is composed of a group of organs which transport food and oxygen to and remove waste from every cell in the body. Blood is the liquid that flows through this system. An adult human contains about ten pints of blood. Blood is made up of a solid part—the cells, and a liquid part—plasma. The solid part is made up of red and white blood cells and blood platelets.

Red blood cells carry oxygen from the lungs and carbon dioxide to the lungs. Red blood cells are produced mainly in bone marrow. Your bones produce about one-half cup of red blood cells daily. Since red blood cells only live about 100–120 days, they must be replaced. Also, aged, damaged, or abnormal cells must be replaced.

White blood cells destroy bacteria and help repair tissue. We have about one white blood cell for every 600 red blood cells.

The liquid portion of the blood is plasma. It is about 90% water and contains protein and dissolved salts. As part of the blood, it moves through the veins and arteries.

The heart acts as the pump of the circulatory system. It keeps the blood moving endlessly through the body. There are four main parts of the heart which are divided into two distinct halves—right and

29

left. Inside each half are two chambers. The top one is the atrium which receives the blood and acts as a tiny reservoir. When the heart relaxes, the blood is pulled into the lower chamber called the ventricle. A valve, like a one-way door, keeps the blood from backing up into the atrium. When the heart contracts, the blood is pushed out of the heart. Another valve keeps the blood from running back into the ventricle. The "heartbeat" that is heard through a stethoscope is the opening and closing of these valves.

The veins carry blood to the heart and appear to be a darker color because of the lack of oxygen. The arteries carry blood away from the heart and are rich in oxygen from the lungs. Arteries are bright red in color. After blood completes its journey through the heart, it is in the left ventricle. From there, it is ready to flow into the aorta for its trip around the body.

Since this trip is so much longer than the round trip to the lungs, the left ventricle must pump much more powerfully than the right. This is why the heartbeat is felt on the left side of the body even though the heart is in the center of the body. The muscles are also much thicker on the left side, as can be seen in the heart diagram.

After oxygenated blood reaches the aorta, it flows into branch arteries leading to the head, arms, stomach, intestines, liver, kidneys and all inside organs. Other branches carry blood into the legs and feet. It travels first in large arteries, then smaller ones, and finally into the tiniest blood vessels of all—the capillaries. Here it drops its food and oxygen and picks up waste products from the body cells. It is now deoxygenated blood and is dark red or bluish in color. It passes into tiny veins that lead to larger veins and finally back into the right atrium. This complete trip takes less than a minute to complete.

Pages 15–18: The nervous system has two main divisions: the central nervous system and the peripheral nervous system. The central nervous system consists of the brain and the spinal cord. It controls behavior. The peripheral nervous system includes the nerves which come from the spinal cord and the base of the brain to the different parts of the body.

The peripheral nervous system is the pathway to the brain for the five senses. By sending messages to and from the brain, the nervous system keeps the numerous parts and organs of your body working together—helping you respond to the world around you.

The peripheral nervous system serves the internal organs and controls such activities as digestion, excretion, respiration, circulation, reproduction, and endocrine gland activity.

The individual nerve cell, or neuron, is the basic unit that carries out the work of the nervous system.

Brain cells cannot grow back once destroyed by injury, disease, or birth defects. The damage is irreversible.

Pages 19–22: The framework of the body is the bony and flexible skeleton. It is made up of 206 bones. Bones contain living tissue, cells, blood vessels, mineral deposits which provide hardness, and water. Most of the bones are porous and hollow. This makes bones weigh less and makes it easier for us to get around. Bones are amazingly strong for their weight. Because they are porous, bones are resilient and resistant to blows and shocks.

Bones are made up mostly of a special balance of calcium and phosphorus salts obtained from the diet. If the ratio of required substances is upset by an improper diet, the bones may grow too hard and brittle, or may become too soft and bend. A proper diet is necessary to maintain strong, healthy bones. As people age, their bones become lighter and more brittle because calcium seeps out of the bones gradually. For this reason, older people may break bones more easily than younger people.

Pages 23–25: Nearly half of body weight is muscle weight. The 206 bones of the skeletal framework are covered by nearly 650 muscles. Muscles are composed of many bundles of stringy fibers bound together in bunches. They are connected to bones by tendons, which are tough, elastic-type bands of connective tissue.

Muscles, when stimulated by a nerve to act, contract and produce body heat. Muscles also produce a chemical called lactic acid if the muscles

MP3408 Body Systems

work a long time. This acid causes muscles to become tired. In order to strengthen muscles, plenty of daily, vigorous exercise for short periods, with gradually more effort each time, is necessary. Muscle

fiber increases in size with use—not in number as once thought. Muscles not exercised will shrivel and become weak. This deterioration can happen over a short period of time.

ANSWERS

Page 3
1. to take in oxygen and remove carbon dioxide
2. Cells are working faster and need more oxygen to function. You breathe faster to take in the extra oxygen needed.
3. warmed   cleaned or filtered   moistened
4. oxygen   carbon dioxide

Page 5
1. digestion
2. mouth, salivary glands
3. tongue
4. esophagus, stomach
5. blood stream
6. small intestines
7. duodenum
8. liver, gall bladder
9. pancreas
10. large intestine
11. rectum, anus

Page 6
1. mouth
2. tongue
3. esophagus
4. stomach
5. duodenum
6. small intestine
7. large intestine
8. rectum
9. anus
10. The stomach is churning, grinding, and mashing food as it mixes with digestive juices.
11. It must stay long enough to allow for proper chemical action to break down the food.

Page 8
1. ribs
2. bladder
3. ureters
4. urethra
5. artery
6. D
7. C
8. F
9. A
10. G
11. H
12. B
13. E

Page 10
1. Red blood cells carry oxygen and carbon dioxide.
2. White blood cells destroy bacteria.

3. Blood platelets aid blood clotting.
4. The heart is the pump of the circulatory system.
5. The fluid of the circulatory system is blood.
6. Capillaries are the smallest blood vessels.
7. Arteries lead away from the heart.
8. Veins lead to the heart
9. The circulatory system brings food and oxygen to cells.
10. Plasma is the liquid part of blood.

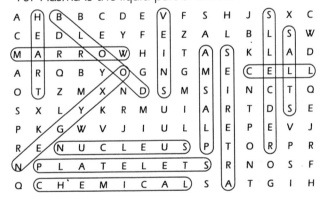

Page 13
See student pages 11 and 12.

Page 14
1. It acts as the pump that keeps the blood moving through the body.
2. Veins
3. Arteries
4. aorta
5. A. superior vena cava
   B. right atrium
   C. right ventricle
   D. pulmonary artery
   E. pulmonary vein
   F. left atrium
   G. left ventricle
   H. aorta

6. red blood cells
7. white blood cells
8. platelets
9. plasma
10. The lungs take carbon dioxide and water from the blood in exchange for oxygen to be carried to all body cells.
11. bluish, red. Your body may not be able to replace the lost blood fast enough to supply the cells with the necessary oxygen to maintain life.

Page 17
1. protects eye from strong light and foreign objects
2. protects finger from further injury or burns
3. allows more oxygen to be sent to cells that need it because of increased activity
4. rids body of materials no longer of use as nourishment
5. This is the first step in digestion and the breaking down of foods into useful material for the body cells.
6. gets rid of something unpleasant in your mouth that could be harmful or make you ill
7. acts as an early warning signal that there may be an invasion of germs somewhere in the body

Page 18
1. A. brain
   B. spinal cord
   C. nerves
2. The brain receives messages from the sense organs and controls movements and activities.
3. skull, spinal column
4. A. I   F. V
   B. V   G. V
   C. V   H. I
   D. I   I. V
   E. I   J. I
5. Brain cells cannot grow back once they are destroyed.
6. neuron   9. medulla
7. cerebrum   10. reflex
8. cerebellum

Page 20
1. A. supports structure
   B. gives shape
   C. protects organs
   D. provides attachment for muscles

2. periosteum
3. 2 hips, 2 arms
4. 2 knees, 2 elbows
5. wrists or spine
6. head on spine and shoulders
7. skull

Page 21
1. clavicle   6. skull
2. kneecap   7. sternum
3. tibia, fibula   8. pelvis
4. radius, ulna   9. femur
5. shoulders, hips 10. jawbone or mandible
11. The joints can only swing in one direction, like a hinge on a door.
12. A. supports structure
    B. protects organs
    C. gives shape
    D. provides attachment for muscles
13. 206
14. axial, appendicular

Page 22
1. D   6. A
2. I   7. C
3. J   8. H
4. E   9. F
5. G   10. B
11. They allow us to move.
12. It is the major supporting bone and it protects the spinal cord.
13. It supports your body, gives you shape, and is strong.
14. As people age, calcium gradually seeps out of their bones. Bones become light and brittle and break easily.
15. A proper diet ensures the balance of calcium, which is needed to keep the bones from becoming hard and brittle or too soft.

Page 24
1. B   4. B   7. B   10. B
2. B   5. A   8. C   11. B
3. A   6. A   9. A   12. B